Birds in quarries and gravel pits

Flying gemstones and swift hunters

Editor

Dr. Michael Rademacher,
Global Manager Biodiversity & Natural Resources, HeidelbergCement

Written by

INULA – Institut für Naturschutz und Landschaftsanalyse, Freiburg i. Br.

ISBN 978-3-9815050-4-7

1st edition, 2013

Table of contents

Preface

Dear reader,

the third volume in our series about habitats in quarries and gravel pits deals with a group of animals of unchallenged popularity: the birds.

The behaviour and biology of these undisputed monarchs of the air has fascinated people for millennia. Birds have inspired philosophers and artists, and throughout Europe birds such as swallows and cranes, swans and geese have been celebrated as heralds of the changing seasons.

Scientists are also drawn to birds, and the challenges they present to our understanding. For example, bird migration is one of the most complex phenomena in nature, involving the ability to navigate in three-dimensional space over distances of hundreds and thousands of kilometres, often in darkness, and sometimes without the benefit of visible landmarks.

Birds such as chickens and other poultry play an important role in human diet, to the point that as you read this, there are at least four chickens alive for you and every other person on the Earth. Beyond this practical use as food, and as bedding and clothing materials, people have found pleasure, consolation and spiritual refreshment in the beautiful plumage and the songs of many bird species. Birds provide scientists with subjects of study that help us understand how the world works, and cast light on our own behaviour.

Because they are easy to study, and react quickly to change, birds are valuable indicators of the state of our environment. Trends in the presence and populations of birds can be used to monitor the health of the ecosystems upon which we humans also depend for the essentials of life, such as clean water, natural foods and other materials, the neutralisation of pollutants, and even the stability of our climate. We can use the insights we derive from monitoring bird populations to take effective action to improve conditions for birds and biodiversity in general, and thereby also for our own benefit.

Birds are crucial for all types of environmental impact studies and plans. Studies of bird populations are important when assessing the impact of a project on an area, and for monitoring the success of measures to reduce or compensate for the impact. This is as true for quarrying and other mineral extraction projects as for any other activity with large-scale effects on the landscape.

Through the process of mineral extraction, bird habitats are lost. But just a few months after work comes to an end, the first bird species will colonise or re-occupy the sites. Little Ringed Plovers breed on exposed gravel plains, Eagle Owls occupy niches in older rock faces, and Sand Martins dig new tunnels for their nests in steep sandy slopes. As the vegetation develops over time, the composition of the bird communities in quarries also changes, from those characteristic of open areas to those of transitional habitats such as scrub. Finally, typical forest birds will occupy the abandoned quarry.

Since some of our mineral extraction sites have been in use for many decades, and include areas where the vegetation is at different stages of regeneration and recovery, their bird communities are often very species-rich. Sites providing specialised conditions which are maintained over long periods of time can be an Eldorado for spectacular species with limited occurrences in Central Europe, such as Bee-eaters and Wallcreepers. Flooded gravel pits provide important resting and feeding sites for breeding, migrating and overwintering waterbirds.

This is the second year of our cooperation with BirdLife International. We are very pleased that our partner has supported this book so enthusiastically. Apart from the scientific revision of the text, we are especially thankful for the many fantastic photos supplied by BirdLife Partner organisations. This successful book project is another proof that our partnership thrives and blossoms.

Enjoy your reading!

Dr. Michael Rademacher
Global Manager Biodiversity and Natural Resources
Programme Director BirdLife Cooperation

Greetings

Dear reader,

This book is only one of the results of the partnership between BirdLife and HeidelbergCement, two organisations with seemingly completely different missions that work together to achieve a common goal – preserving and promoting biodiversity at quarries and pits where millions of tonnes of building materials are extracted for the creation of our own human habitat.

My first experience in a quarry was about 30 years ago, when every Saturday, after my university course ended for the day, I went to an ancient Roman quarry south of Rome. The quarry hosted climbing walls, and a few climbers like me enjoyed the serene environment it offered. Since then I have discovered that the dry environment is also ideal for hosting a number of unique plant and animal species. These memories were fresh in my mind when, several years later, I rediscovered the beauty of nature in quarries thanks to the BirdLife partnership with HeidelbergCement.

For those of you who have read the first two books in the series on Life in the Quarry by HeidelbergCement, about dragonflies and orchids, it will come as no surprise that a great number of rare plants and animals find suitable living conditions in quarries. The fact that cement quarries have great potential to support biodiversity is well known to the mineral extraction industry, scientists and conservationists alike.

We are pleased to share this story of Birds in Quarries with you. Birds are undoubtedly among the most admired living creatures on our planet. Birds give us unprecedented opportunity to study the natural world, and inspire us to conserve it. They are widespread, abundant and adaptable, yet they are delicate and vulnerable creatures. Their behaviour, life history and interactions with the surrounding world are among the best-studied aspects of modern ecology. Yet their flight, song and beauty have never ceased to amaze us. There is hardly a traditional culture or modern art form that has not reserved some space for birds among its objects of admiration. No wonder that the observation, photography and enjoyment of birds are the passions of millions of people around the world. In fact, the beautiful photographs that illustrate this book were kindly contributed by amateur and professional photographers who enthusiastically joined us in this project.

I hope this book will inspire nature lovers to look at quarries with new eyes and, maybe, visit those which have been restored, in search of the beautiful species that have found there a new and even richer habitat.

Angelo Caserta,
Regional Director, BirdLife Europe

HEIDELBERGCEMENT

Partners to enhance biodiversity in quarries

Based on shared values of sustainably using natural resources, BirdLife International and HeidelbergCement have joined forces in a three-year Partnership to promote the thriving biodiversity of quarries. By cooperating at local, national and international levels BirdLife International actively contributes to implement HeidelbergCement's ambitious aspirations to become a leader in biodiversity management at mining sites.

BirdLife International brings worldwide expertise on birds and biodiversity conservation to the Partnership. These priorities fit well with HeidelbergCement's approach to the important role biodiversity plays at quarries based on growing scientific knowledge.

During the first three years, the Partnership targets the development and implementation of a Biodiversity Conservation Programme in Europe and Central Asia.

2012: Sites, species and habitats of highest priority and conservation potential have been identified. These are to be gradually integrated into the standard biodiversity practices at quarry sites via Biodiversity Management Plans.

2013: New conservation projects involving HeidelbergCement's local management and national BirdLife partners will be implemented.

2014: Progress will be evaluated and assessed for replication for other regions where HeidelbergCement is active.

The BirdLife Partnership not only facilitates the exchange of knowledge and conservation expertise with HeidelbergCement, it also assists in establishing a network of essential stakeholders.

BirdLife Partners located in the Partnership countries will have access to the necessary information and additional resources to implement conservation actions in areas with high biodiversity potential. The impact of our partnership will be measured directly by the diversity of plants and animals on the HeidelbergCement quarries!

Flying gemstones and swift hunters

Of birds and men

02

03

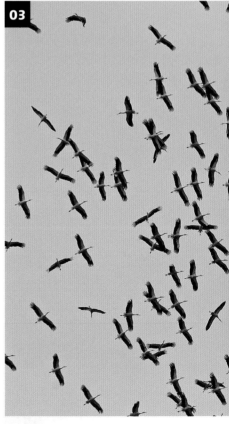

01

Human beings have always been fascinated by birds. Their skilful flight, enchanting songs and beautiful plumage make them one of the showiest and most attractive groups of the animal kingdom.

01 The White Stork (*Ciconia ciconia*) has played an important role in mythology and popular belief. In Roman and Greek mythology, for instance, it was believed that storks did not die of old age, but flew to islands where they turned into humans.

02 In ancient Greece, the Little Owl (*Athene noctua*) was considered a symbol of wisdom and thus associated with the goddess Athene. Hence its scientific name, *Athene noctua*.

03 The sight of migrating birds has always stirred the human imagination. In ancient Rome, priests predicted the future by observing them.

04 More often heard than seen, the Common Cuckoo (*Cuculus canorus*) is named after the characteristic call of the male.

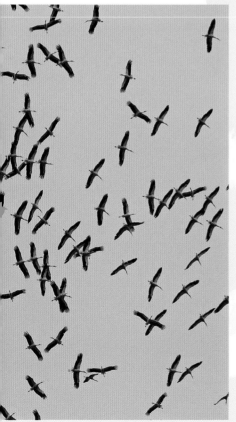

Birds in arts, culture and science

Birds play an important role in folk songs and stories, fables and mythology, and birdsong has inspired composers, thinkers, and artists.

Ta, ta, ta, TAA!!! The opening of Beethoven's Fifth Symphony is believed to be based on the song of the Ortolan Bunting (*Emberiza hortulana*).

Birds occur in many sayings and figures of speech, such as "The early bird catches the worm", "A bird in hand is worth two in the bush", and "One swallow does not make a summer".

Birds are also important symbols in popular belief, superstition and religious iconography. The dove is a symbol of peace in many cultures. According to European folklore, the stork brings babies to new parents, and storks which nest on buildings bring good luck.

Birds are also important sources for technology. Leonardo da Vinci's designs for flying machines were based on his studies of bird flight. Today, the structures of bird bones and feathers provide ideas and blueprints for bionics (or bio-mimicry), an interdisciplinary science integrating biology, materials science and engineering.

01

01 Catch you later! A young Barn Swallow (*Hirundo rustica*) peers at potential prey.

02 The House Sparrow (*Passer domesticus*) is one of our most familiar birds, but not as common as it used to be. This photo shows a male.

03 The Eurasian Blackbird (*Turdus merula*) has made a success of living alongside humans. There are often more breeding pairs in town gardens than in comparable areas of woodland.

02

Flagships of nature conservation

Birds carry on their lives in the open, and usually in daylight, and can be easily watched by anyone who has a few minutes to spare. Many have adapted well to urban environments, substituting houses for cliffs, and gardens for forests, singing from our rooftops, and coming readily to bird tables and feeding stations. Birdwatching has become one of the world's most popular hobbies, and many biologists and conservationists started their careers as passionate birdwatchers. Amateur birders can make an important contribution as citizen scientists, or help monitor and manage sites that are important for birds.

03

The dinosaurs are still among us!

Birds are a relatively old animal group. They originated during the heyday of the dinosaurs, in the Jurassic period, about 200 to 145 million years ago. Their evolutionary development has only recently begun to be understood, and is revealing some startling relationships. Newly discovered fossils have shown that crocodiles are more closely related to birds than to lizards and snakes. Phylogenetically, birds and crocodiles belong to the dinosaurs, and are thus living representatives of this group! These discoveries have really shaken the family tree of the vertebrates as biologists thought they knew them, and the term "reptiles", as we still use it commonly, has been shown to be basically wrong.

01

03

01 It is hard to believe that this delicate Blue Tit (*Parus caeruleus*) is a relative of dinosaurs…

02 …while these young Purple Herons (*Ardea purpurea*) really do look like something from the Jurassic.

03 Is this a Velociraptor's foot? No. It belongs to a chicken (*Gallus gallus domesticus*).

01 The Cinereous Vulture (*Aegypius monachus*) is the biggest of all Old World raptors, with a beak to match.

Primeval birds and transitional fossils

Archaeopteryx is a fossil with feathers. It was dug up in Germany in 1861 and is considered a **transitional fossil** between dinosaurs and birds.

Transitional fossils are connecting links between different species or species groups. They display the older traits of the original species as well as new traits of the younger species.

Archaeopteryx was about as big as a chicken, and lived about 150 million years ago. Its long tail, teeth and fingers with claws are original dinosaur features, while its bird features include backward pointing toes, air-filled bones, and above all, feathers.

01

Recently discovered fossils, mostly from China, indicate that there were many dinosaur species with feathers before and during the time of Archaeopteryx. It is now questionable whether Archaeopteryx is really an ancestor, or just a remote cousin of the birds.

In any case, Archaeopteryx and other fossils with feathers give clues about the evolution of modern birds. An important question is: How did the ability to fly develop? Although able to glide short distances, the "primeval bird" was not yet capable of active flight. Feathers must then have had a different function, such as protection and insulation of the skin, or adornments used in courtship. The ability to fly developed later, as a kind of by-product of plumage.

Archaeopteryx

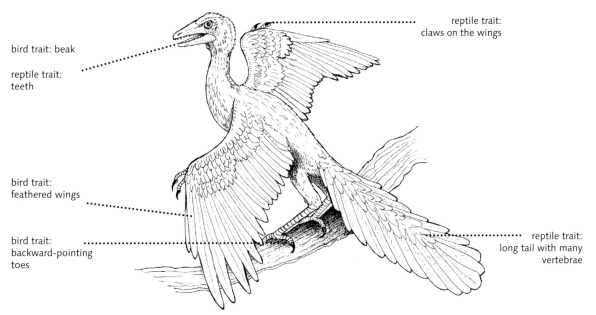

bird trait: beak

reptile trait: teeth

reptile trait: claws on the wings

bird trait: feathered wings

bird trait: backward-pointing toes

reptile trait: long tail with many vertebrae

Drawing of Archaeopteryx. Drawn after Cummings (Pearson Education).

Birds are (almost) everywhere

Birds form one of the largest vertebrate groups. There are more than 10,300 species inhabiting all kinds of habitats. Forests, steppes, coasts, mountains, and deserts – there is almost no place that is not visited or colonised by birds, at least temporarily. Accordingly, the shapes and sizes and lifestyles of individual bird species are very diverse, from ostriches taller than men to hummingbirds smaller than bumblebees, and from the humble grey or brown species of fields and steppes to the breathtaking blazes of colour which light up tropical forests. Some spend almost all their lives at sea, others live in the world's driest places. Some feed and breed in places, such as saline lakes, that are hostile to almost all other vertebrate life. Others live near the tops of the world's highest mountains, or fly over them.

01

01 Like a flying barn door: the White-tailed Eagle (*Heliaeetus albicilla*) is one of the biggest raptors in Europe.

World of extremes – bird records

Though incapable of flying, the Ostrich holds many bird records. At 2.50 metres in height and up to 150 kg in weight, it is the tallest and heaviest bird on Earth. It also has the longest legs (1.50 m), and is the fastest runner (over 70 km/h). Its eyes, with a diameter of 5 cm, are the biggest of any bird.

The smallest bird on Earth, the Bee Hummingbird (*Mellisuga helenae*), is just a little bit longer than the diameter of an Ostrich's eye (5.7 cm). This tiny hummingbird species occurs exclusively on Cuba. It weighs around 1.6 g and lays the smallest eggs: they are pea-sized, measuring only 6.7 mm in length.

The Common Swift (fig. 03, p. 23) leaves the skies only briefly, during the breeding season. From fledging until their first breeding, these birds are airborne for almost three years; they even sleep in the air. The Common Swift's legs are the shortest of all birds, at 1 cm. Its feet are ideal for clinging to rough vertical surfaces, but almost incapable of walking. In flight, its ability to manoeuvre at speeds of up to 100 km/h is unsurpassed. But for sheer speed it is overtaken by the Peregrine Falcon (fig. 03, p. 78), which can reach over 160 km/h as it plunges through the air towards its prey, making it the fastest bird (and creature) alive.

02 The Eurasian Wren (*Troglodytes troglodytes*) is barely ten centimetres from its needle-like beak to its stumpy tail.

03 The world's tallest bird. This female Ostrich (*Struthio camelus*) towers over the photographer.

Birds and their beaks

01 The crossed mandibles from which the Red Crossbill (*Loxia curvirostra*) gets its name are used to separate the scales of spruce and pine cones and pull out the seeds.

02 The Great Spotted Woodpecker (*Dendrocopos major*) uses its strong chisel-like beak to expose insect larvae in dead wood.

Bird's beaks are effective tools which show amazing adaptations to the feeding behaviour and diet of individual species.

03 The massive hooked beaks of large raptors like the White-tailed Eagle (*Haliaeetus albicilla*) are adapted to tearing lumps of meat out of their prey.

04 The tweezer-like beak of the Short-toed Treecreeper (*Certhia brachydactyla*) is designed to pick small insects from under the scales of coarse tree bark.

05 Waders like the Eurasian Curlew (*Numenius arquata*) use their long beaks to probe the mud in search of worms and molluscs. Standing on one leg reduces heat loss and helps save energy.

03

04

05

Winging it

All birds have wings. Their flying abilities, however, differ greatly, from the hectic flapping of ducks via the swift-as-an-arrow swoops of falcons to the soaring and gliding of storks.

Even flightless birds have wings or wing stubs, and it is assumed that the ancestors of all birds, including ratite birds (such as ostriches) and penguins, could once fly.

01 The Common Kestrel (*Falco tinnunculus*) mainly hunts by hovering, but will also pounce on prey from a perch.

01

Birdbrains? As if! About bird intelligence.

Birds are pretty smart. Jays can memorise the locations of countless caches of acorns by using landmarks. The sense of orientation of hunting birds of prey and of migratory birds also demonstrates a highly-developed brain.

As mimics, the talent of starlings, parrots, and jackdaws and other crows is legendary. The behaviourist Irene Pepperberg had a Grey Parrot (*Psittacus erithacus*) called Alex (1976 - 2007), which gained fame because it was able to count to six and to distinguish between seven colours and five geometric shapes. Moreover, it had an active vocabulary of 200 human words.

Some birds are tool users, demonstrating the kind of intelligence otherwise only found in some apes and a few other primates. In wild populations of New Caledonian Crows (*Corvus moneduloides*), some individuals tear off the thorny edges of palm leaves and use them as barbed hooks with which they poke around for larvae in rotten wood. Learning this technique is difficult and time-consuming; however, the offspring imitate it, so that this behaviour is passed on within the population.

02 The Eurasian Jay (*Garrulus glandarius*) is a skilled solver of problems it encounters when foraging, and a gifted mimic.

03 The Common Swift (*Apus apus*) is so well adapted to life in the sky that it sleeps on the wing, staying airborne for months or even years.

The feather: from insulation to aerofoil

01

Vane feathers are distinguished from down feathers, which have soft quills and barbules lacking hooks. Down feathers are fluffy and provide great thermal insulation. There are other more specialised feathers, such as bristle feathers which protect the eyes, and powder-down feathers, which produce water-repellent "feather dust" in ducks, doves, and herons. Some feathers are hairlike, with strongly innervated quills and sensory functions.

Feathers are exclusive to birds. They are not derived from reptile scales, as long believed, but evolved independently. They are made of keratin, the protein that also forms our nails and hair. Feathers protect birds from heat and cold and have species-specific colours and patterns. They can serve as camouflage to hide from predators, or have features such as crests that are used for communication with others of their species.

Of course, feathers are also indispensable for flight. Tail feathers are used for steering, while the robust primary and secondary feathers of the wings act as flexible aerofoils. These feathers, and the contour feathers that cover the body, are formed of a rigid shaft (rachis), and horizontal branches known as barbs. The barbs in turn carry smaller barbules, bearing tiny hooks which interlock each barb with its neighbours to form a web, or vane.

01 The drake Mallard (*Anas platyrhynchos*) shakes its bright green, shining head during its courtship display. Preen oil makes its feathers water-repellent.

Structure of a feather

vaned feather (pinion feather)

down feather

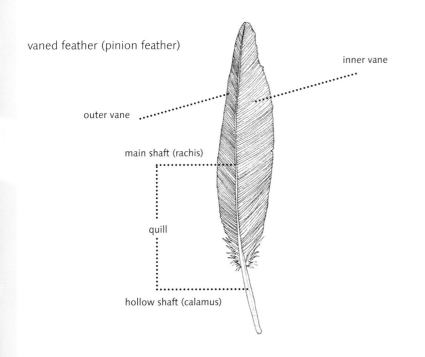

inner vane

outer vane

main shaft (rachis)

quill

hollow shaft (calamus)

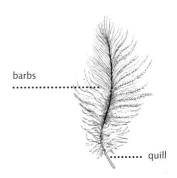

barbs

quill

02

02 A Stock Dove (*Columba oenas*) spreads its tail to apply the brakes as it comes in to land.

01 European Rollers (*Coracias garrulus*) offer wedding gifts.

02 As in many other birds, male Common Pheasants (*Phasianus colchicus*) are more colourful and conspicuous than their females.

Courtship and breeding behaviour

Male birds advertise themselves to the females with songs and displays, and court them with gifts of food and nesting material. The more gorgeous the plumage, the more energetic the courtship dance, the more beautifully decorated the nest, the more attractive is a male bird. The female is able to choose the healthiest and most robust males, which will father the fittest offspring with the best chances of survival. In some species the males are also demonstrating that they are good partners to help the female raise her brood successfully.

03 The male Eurasian Penduline Tit (*Remiz pendulinus*) builds several elaborate hanging nests. The female picks the one she likes the best.

03

Nests and nest sites

Many bird species build their nests in vegetation like trees and bushes, or reed beds. The nests may be cup shaped, or domed, or hanging pendants. Others are platforms which may be added to in successive breeding seasons, until, like the nests of some White Storks (fig. 01, p. 10), they can reach hundreds of kilograms in weight.

Ground-breeding birds: Some birds, like the Little Ringed Plover, do not build a nest at all. Instead, they lay their well-camouflaged eggs in scrapes in sand or shingle. Throughout Europe, such ground-breeding birds are in trouble, because suitable breeding areas such as river banks, sand and gravel plains, fallow fields and other bare or sparsely-vegetated places are being rapidly converted for intensive agriculture, or built over for settlements and infrastructure. Even when they manage to nest, many of their young fall victim to agricultural machines or predators.

Cavity nesters are also having a hard time. Many use cavities made by woodpeckers, or caused by the rotting of old trees. But such big old trees are becoming more and more exceptional because of the short rotation periods in modern forestry, and the seemingly irresistible urge of local authorities to make public woodlands and parks tidy. Old trees forming avenues along roads are often removed for safety reasons.

Many species which today build their nests on houses and other buildings, such as House Sparrows, Black Redstarts, Common Swifts, Barn Owls and Common Kestrels were originally **cliff** or **rock breeders**. It is becoming increasingly difficult for these species to find suitable sites for nesting: modern houses are built without loft spaces, and old buildings that remain are refurbished to modern standards, which often include sealing the gaps and holes the birds once used.

01 An Osprey (*Pandion haliaetus*) feeding its chicks.

02 The Little Ringed Plover (*Charadrius dubius*) does not build a real nest. Instead, it lays its perfectly camouflaged eggs in a nest scraped in bare, gravelly ground.

03 First out: a Eurasian Coot (*Fulica atra*) hatchling sprawls on the eggs of its slower siblings. Young coots are ready to take to the water almost at once (nidifugous).

01

Nidicolous (altricial) and nidifugous (precocial) birds

All birds lay eggs and care for their broods, though some young birds are far more dependent on their parents than others.

Nidicolous hatchlings are blind and naked and have to be fed and kept warm by their parents until they are fully fledged. Typical representatives are Great Tits (fig. 03, p. 92) and Carrion Crows (*Corvus corone*). Crows are – contrary to common belief – exceptionally caring parents.

Nidifugous birds hatch covered with down feathers and fully-developed eyes and ears. In many cases they can run, feed, swim and dive directly after hatching. Usually they stay in the nest for only one or two days, then leave it together with their mother, and do not return. The hatchlings stay together with their siblings and one or both parents for a short period of time, but soon start their own independent lives. Ground-nesting species like ducks and wading birds (including the Little Ringed Plover, described above) are typical nidifugous birds.

01 A Mute Swan chick (*Cygnus olor*) cruises around on its father's back.

02 A Greylag Goose pair (*Anser anser*) with goslings.

03 A male Northern Wheatear (*Oenanthe oenanthe*) on its guard before feeding the begging chick.

They call me the wanderer...

01

02

Bird migration is one of the most fascinating of natural spectacles. Every year hundreds of millions of birds leave their breeding grounds to spend the winter in warmer regions with better food resources.

Migratory birds cover long distances, trusting in their outstanding sense of orientation. They have a magnetic sense which is still not fully understood. There are indications that their beaks contain small iron particles helping the birds to sense the magnetic field of the Earth and determine their position at any time. Birds are probably capable of literally seeing with their eyes the direction of the magnetic lines tracing the sky. A certain protein allows them to detect the north. This helps them to find and stay on their route.

Moreover, some migratory birds can sense polarised light and use the position of the sun for navigation purposes – even when it is cloudy!

Rivers and mountains, in modern times roads and cities likewise, serve as landmarks. Many birds migrate at night and use the "compass of the stars". Increasing "light pollution", the artificial light emitted by settlements, car headlights and streetlamps, makes orientation more difficult for them.

01 Blackcaps (*Sylvia atricapilla*) are common birds in gardens and parks. Formerly most were short distance migrants, but increasing numbers stay all year round.

02 A beautiful sight, accompanied by characteristic calls: migrating Common Cranes (*Grus grus*) cross the evening sky.

03 Many gardeners enjoy the presence of „their" robin (*Erithacus rubecola*), without realising that the summer and winter birds are likely to be different individuals.

Short and long-distance migration

Some birds are **short-distance**, others **long-distance migrants**. Apart from these there are **sedentary birds** which stay in the same places all the year round, and others which make temporary movements following sudden spells of harsh weather or food shortage, but generally stay in the same geographical area.

The wintering grounds of **long-distance migrants** can be many thousands of kilometres away from their breeding grounds. In order to get there, long and dangerous trips are necessary. The migration direction is determined genetically. Many European long-distance migrants, including some White Storks (fig. 01, p. 10) and Barn Swallows (fig. 01, p. 12), have to cross the Sahara.

Short-distance migrants, however, usually cover distances of not more than 2,000 km. European short-distance migrants, such as European Robins, never cross the Sahara. Instead, they fly to the mild Atlantic coast or to Mediterranean regions. Sometimes one species will include populations or individuals with different migration strategies. For example, some Blackcaps are sedentary, some are short-distance migrants, and some make local movements.

Dangerous journeys

01

02

Migrating birds are continually at risk. In addition to their natural enemies, humans pose a serious threat. Birds are trapped with nets and lime-twigs for Southern European and African cooking pots, or shot by "sportsmen". Climate change, resulting in droughts in their resting sites and overwintering grounds, is becoming more and more problematic. Deserts expand, and in the African Sahel, the wetlands that used to furnish them with abundant food are drying up. Moreover, infrastructure projects and intensified agriculture are leading to the destruction of more and more ecologically valuable areas in the southern hemisphere. Returning birds find the winter habitats they have been using for millennia seriously degraded or even destroyed.

01 Danger for a near-threatened species: curlew decoys on a beach in France.

02 A dead Northern Goshawk (*Accipiter gentilis*). Collisions with power lines or cars are typical causes of death for migrating birds.

03

04

03 The European Honey Buzzard (*Pernis apivorus*) migrates by soaring in thermals. When crossing the Sahara, it increases its speed to travel 270 kilo-metres a day.

04 Common Starlings (*Sturnus vulgaris*) are very sociable and form huge flocks during migration periods.

Conserving birds in Europe

More than 500 bird species have been recorded in Europe. Species that specialise in particular habitats, such as wetlands and heaths, are becoming increasingly rare. But the populations of many bird species still considered common are also decreasing. There are numerous reasons: intensification of forestry and agriculture, urban sprawl and other kinds of habitat destruction, and hunting in breeding or wintering areas or along the migration routes. Birds are in urgent need of protection, and since they are good indicators of the condition of ecosystems, bird protection is equally favourable for many other animal and plant species.

01

01 An idyllic view of wetlands.

02 The introduced Egyptian Goose (*Alopochen aegyptiacus*) adds colour to European bird life. During the breeding season, these geese are strictly territorial.

Invasive species

Species introduced from other parts of the world, either accidentally (like rats) or deliberately (like deer) can establish themselves in places where conditions are right (and their natural predators are absent), and become a threat to native species. In fact, alien predators and pathogens have been implicated in almost half of all bird extinctions in the last 500 years. Newcomers can also outcompete closely-related native species. In Europe, the native White-headed Duck (*Oxyura leucocephala*) is threatened by hybridisation with the more dominant Ruddy Duck (*Oxyura jamaicensis*), which was introduced from North America.

Nature conservation in quarries and gravel pits

Mineral extraction activities such as quarries and gravel diggings always mean great changes in a landscape. Existing landscapes are changed permanently, and plants and animals are expelled. However, although they look barren and empty at first, within a relatively short period of time mineral extraction sites may develop into completely new, valuable habitats for specialised animal and plant species.

02

01

03

01 Common House Martins (*Delichon urbicum*) build their nests out of mud. Shallow shore zones are important sources of construction material.

02 Maiden pink (*Dianthus deltoides*) grows on nutrient-poor soils in quarries and gravel pits.

03 View of a quarry with rock faces and unconsolidated materials.

Natural flood plains – vanishing pristine landscapes

01   **02**

Change ruled in the vast alluvial plains of pristine post-glacial landscapes. Rivers frequently switched their courses, in beds that were up to 10 km wide. Within this dynamic space, the landscape was in a constant state of flux.

Floodwaters uprooted trees, eroded banks and deposited gravel and sand. When the waters receded, flooded grassland, ponds and open gravel areas remained – ideal conditions for pioneer and specialist species. Rivers often changed their course so

completely that the next high water affected completely different areas of the alluvial zone.

01 The Yellow-bellied Toad (*Bombina variegata*) evolved its breeding habits in the dynamic landscapes of Europe's pristine river flood-plains. It now depends on temporary bodies of water such as puddles in tyre-tracks.

02 The Common Kingfisher (*Alcedo atthis*) is a typical inhabitant of slow-flowing rivers. It also occurs at flooded mineral extraction sites with abundant fish.

03 Standing water with reed zone.

04 A pair of Little Terns (*Sterna albifrons*) in a gravel pit.

Today, almost all rivers and streams in Europe are straightened and regulated. Dynamic processes have been reduced almost to zero. The vast alluvial forests are gone except for a few remnants, and the specialised habitats of floodplains, along with their plant and animal communities, are severely threatened. "Renaturalising" rivers and restoring their floodplains and alluvial habitats are important tasks for nature protection, but can also help protect human settlements from floods.

You've got to move it, move it... dynamics in quarries and gravel pits

Today, in most regions of Europe, dynamics comparable to the conditions in natural floodplains can be found almost exclusively in mineral extraction sites. The mineral extraction process creates vast gravel plains, steep slopes, and large and small bodies of water. These can serve as secondary habitats for a variety of – often rare – plant and animal species of alluvial plains and associated ecosystems. Standing waters in quarries and gravel pits are of great importance for dragonflies, amphibians, and many bird species, and large flooded gravel pits can be important resting places for migrating waterfowl and waders.

01 Ponds with shallow inundation zones and reedmace (*Typha*) at a mineral extraction site.

02 Greylag Geese (*Anser anser*) at a gravel pit.

Loss of floodplains and the intensification of land use.

A **primary habitat** is the site where an animal or plant species occurred before human impact altered the landscape. The primary habitats of many plant and animal species that are threatened today lay within pristine floodplains. Some birds depend for breeding on open riverside forests, or on gravel shores and eroded river banks, but all these specialised habitats have been reduced to a fraction of their former extent throughout most of Europe. That is why bird species adapted to floodplains are nowadays often dependent on **secondary habitats**.

Some floodplain plant and animal species find favourable conditions within agricultural landscapes: meadows, pastures, ploughed fields or fallows. The soil is disturbed (ploughed) periodically, and nutrient input (fertilisation) is high. Early in the year, when the crops are still low, stony fields can be similar to former inundation zones, providing good breeding conditions for some bird species.

But the demand for continuous increases in productivity has led to the intensification of agriculture. This has caused the deterioration of the human-made cultural landscapes to which many plant and animal species have adapted themselves over the centuries. Today, large-scale monocultures with intensive use of pesticides, herbicides, and fertilisers prevail. Copses, shrubs, fallow strips, and semi-natural grasslands are becoming rarer. "Improvement" of meadows and pastures by fertilisation and ploughing causes great problems for ground-nesting birds, leading to denser grassy vegetation or crops, which fledglings are unable to move through. Because of pesticides, parents cannot find enough insects for their chicks. Most meadows are mowed more than twice per year, making it impossible for meadow-breeding birds to raise their chicks.

All these factors have led to strong declines even among species that used to be abundant everywhere, such as Eurasian Skylarks (*Alauda arvensis*) and Northern Lapwings (*Vanellus vanellus*). These species may however find the conditions they need in carefully managed mineral extraction sites.

03

03 Black-headed Gulls (*Larus ridibundus*) can be watched at large gravel pit lakes.

Quarries and gravel pits provide homes and resting places for displaced birds

Many bird species find important secondary habitats in mineral extraction sites. Birds often have large daily ranges, so areas of scrub or gravel plains may represent only a fraction of the overall habitat they need. Especially for breeding birds that must gather sufficient food for their chicks, the surroundings of quarries and gravel pits are of great importance. Birds profit from good connectivity of the mineral extraction sites with species-rich forests or diverse agricultural landscapes.

01

02

01 A quarry with a mosaic of different habitats.

02 Greater White-fronted Geese (*Anser albifrons*) like to graze in shallow shore zones.

03 The Grey Heron (*Ardea cinerea*) is frequently seen at flooded mineral workings.

04 A Eurasian Jackdaw (*Corvus monedula*) investigates a sandy slope.

Mineral extraction sites adjacent to running waters often possess a particularly great species richness. On the one hand, this has to do with the fact that even degraded floodplains are often comparatively well-equipped with diverse habitats. On the other hand, many birds follow traditional migration routes along the rivers. Gravel pits can be important, in many cases offering the only undisturbed resting areas.

Bird habitats

General rule:

If nesting activities are detected in an area, it must be spared from excavation. If mineral extraction in areas colonised by birds is inevitable, it must wait until after the end of the breeding season. Before quarrying, suitable replacement habitats – steep banks, gravel plains etc. – must be created ready for next year's breeding birds.

Large flooded gravel pits

Shallow waters with rich shore vegetation are very important for many migrating duck species like Common Teal and Common Shelducks, or, when fish are abundant, Common Mergansers. Large flocks of migrating geese, too, may spend the nights on the protected water surface of large gravel pit lakes, or search for food along the shorelines.

01

01 Greylag Geese (*Anser anser*) at a gravel pit.

02 The overall population trend of the Common Teal (*Anas crecca*) is uncertain. It has declined in a number of European countries, but remained stable or even increased in others.

03 The Common Shelduck (*Tadorna tadorna*) is mainly a bird of coastal zones, but during migration it can be found on inland gravel pit lakes.

04 Young Common Mergansers (*Mergus merganser*) riding on their mother's back.

Shallow shore zones and ponds

Shallow shore zones and ponds offer important food resources for migrating waders.

01 Muddy edges and shallow water are valuable feeding habitats for waders.

02 Temminck's Stint (*Calidris temminckii*) breeds in the Arctic. Migrating birds may rest and feed on the muddy shores of flooded mineral workings.

03 The Common Snipe (*Gallinago gallinago*) breeds in marshes and wet meadows.

04

05

04 Wood Sandpipers (*Tringa glareola*) overwinter in the tropics. They can be observed resting in gravel pits.

05 Curlew Sandpipers (*Calidris ferruginea*) breed in northern Russia and can be encountered in Central Europe during the winter.

Small lakes with reed zones

Ageing gravel pit lakes and ponds are often characterised by abundant water and shore vegetation. Here, many bird species find excellent retreats and hiding places.

01

02

01 A courting pair of Great Crested Grebes (*Podiceps cristatus*). These are characteristic breeding birds of flooded gravel pits.

02 In small inland ponds and lakes with well-developed floating vegetation the Little Grebe (*Tachchybaptus ruficollis*) may breed.

03 An older gravel pit lake.

01

Reed zones

Lakes in disused gravel pits, with shallow shore zones, wide reed zones, and other types of dense shore vegetation, can be breeding and resting areas for Common Coots, Common Moorhens, and even for Water Rails.

02

01 The Common Moorhen (*Gallinula chloropus*) occurs around nutrient-rich standing waters with dense shore vegetation.

03

02 The Water Rail (*Rallus aquaticus*) is a secretive inhabitant of reedbeds that reveals its presence mainly by its pig-like calls.

03 Water birds like this Eurasian Coot (*Fulica atra*) need a long and strenuous run-up before take-off.

01

02

01 Reed zones are ecologically very important.

02 The Eurasian reed warbler (*Acrocephalus scirpaceus*) is a very common breeding bird in reedbeds, including small stands of reeds in ditches and ponds.

03 A male Reed Bunting (*Emberiza schoeniclus*).

Grey Herons and Great Egrets (*Casmerodius albus*, also called Great White Herons), search for food within wide reed belts. Great Bitterns may rest or even breed in these habitats.

Reed Buntings and several warbler species breed within dense reed zones. Loud, spirited singers, they are hard to miss, though not always easy to locate.

Creation of reed zones

Practical example:

In the gravel pit at Needingworth near Cambridgeshire, a valuable reed zone was created in cooperation with the Royal Society for the Protection of Birds (RSPB, BirdLife's Partner in the UK). The Great Bittern was the main target species of this project.

An area historically drained for agriculture was "re-wetted" and transformed into reedbeds. Areas of between 20 and 40 hectares were recreated and planted with typical reed zone vegetation. A ditch system around the perimeter, with sluice gates, allows for the precise regulation of the water level.

This joint project between Heidelberg-Cement and the RSPB was carried out in close cooperation with citizens from the surrounding communities. Local people were invited to participate in the planning process, and were the first to plant reed seedlings. The newly-created nature protection area was soon made accessible, and since 2008, a network of public hiking, riding and biking paths has attracted visitors from near and far.

Lessons learned from the creation of reed zones for waterfowl in England

At many wet sites, reedbeds develop spontaneously. However, the process may need to be speeded up for reasons of bird protection. The following lessons were learned from the Needingworth project described above (although each project must be planned and carried out individually, according to local conditions and target species).

During the process of reedbed creation, the following aspects should be considered:

- Reed seedlings should be planted in more than 50% of the area.
- High water levels can help control undesired pioneer plant (ruderal) species. Willow seedlings should be pulled out.
- To establish and maintain optimum conditions for the growth of the reeds, water levels should be monitored.
- The development and propagation of the reeds should be monitored. During the early days before the reeds have become established, animals should be kept out of the area by fencing.

Long-term management

- Water levels must be monitored and kept at a level of 15 to 70 cm above the surface to guarantee optimum reed growth.
- The reeds should be cut every ten years to reduce the accumulation of leaf litter and to remove nutrients. The reed stalks should be used commercially if possible.
- Most seedlings of woody plants should be removed, although on around 10% of the whole area the succession of woody plants should be allowed in order to enhance the structural richness of the site.

Monitoring

- Monitoring of breeding birds of high importance for nature conservation.
- Monitoring of overwintering waterfowl.
- Periodic checks of water level and water quality.

03

01 The Great Bittern (*Botaurus stellaris*) is a typical inhabitant of vast reedbeds. In many European countries, its population has not fully recovered from a serious decline throughout much of the 20th Century.

02 A Grey Heron (*Ardea cinerea*) well-hidden in a reed zone.

03 Male Sedge Warblers (*Acrocephalus schoenobaenus*) often sing from exposed perches on tall reeds.

01

Gravel islands and artificial nesting rafts

03

In natural landscapes, Common Terns breed on barren gravel islands in rivers, created by floods. Here, their eggs and chicks are protected from predators.

But today, almost all rivers and streams in Europe have been straightened and regulated so that gravel islands are no longer created, and these birds are becoming rare. Artificial breeding rafts are an excellent substitute that could help to reverse their decline.

01 Outside the breeding season, the Common Tern (*Sterna hirundo*) can be found fishing on flooded gravel pits.

02 Today the Little Tern (*Sterna albifrons*) is mainly restricted to coastal areas. The species once occurred along rivers throughout much of Europe, but lost its habitat as the rivers were straightened and regulated

03 Little Terns breeding on a natural gravel island.

04 Common Terns on an artificial nesting raft made of wood and metal.

Practical example:

Examples for the successful employment of breeding rafts for terns can be found in mineral extraction sites in the Czech Republic and in Germany. The rafts, along with measures to increase fish populations to provide food, have led to an increase in tern breeding success.

Cement raft with protective fence

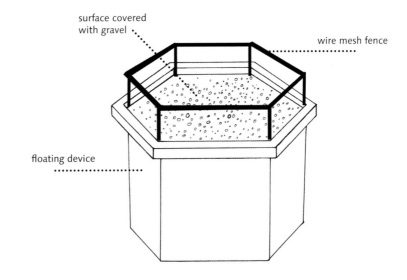

surface covered with gravel

wire mesh fence

floating device

01 These hexagonal artificial cement nesting raft modules can be combined to create larger "islands".

02 Fences that keep out predators provide a safe place to grow up for Common Tern chicks.

Nesting rafts for Common Terns

Floating nesting rafts, covered with gravel and equipped with fences as a protection from predators, can offer safe breeding places for Common Terns, even in deep gravel pit lakes. Ready-made nesting rafts made of wood, steel, or special cement are available, the latter having proven outstandingly long-lasting. The rafts must be anchored securely to keep them from drifting to the shore. Breeding success should be monitored.

Gravel plains and bare ground

Barren or sparsely vegetated plains of gravel or other unconsolidated materials can be important secondary breeding habitats for several bird species.

Little Ringed Plovers and Common Sandpipers are characteristic breeding birds of gravelly river shores. They occur in mineral extraction sites, too.

01

01 A Little Ringed Plover (*Charadrius dubius*) with eight legs? Three chicks sheltering under one of their parents.

02 Sparsely vegetated ground in a quarry.

03 A feathery ball with legs: the chick of the Little Ringed Plover.

02

03

04 The intensification of farming has destroyed or degraded many arable fields and meadows where the Northern Lapwing (*Vanellus vanellus*) once nested and raised its young. Larger gravel pits can offer suitable conditions for these birds to breed and forage.

05 The Common Sandpiper (*Actitis hypoleucos*) sometimes nests among sparse herbaceous vegetation. Its nest is never far from water.

04

05

01 Panorama of a quarry, showing range of habitats.

02 The White Wagtail (*Motacilla alba*) can be observed foraging on open soils close to water.

03 The Common Gull (*Larus canus*) is a rare breeding bird in mineral excavation sites in northern Central Europe. It needs large unvegetated gravel areas to nest and raise its chicks.

04 The Eurasian skylark (*Alauda arvensis*) may breed in mineral excavation sites.

01

Steep unconsolidated rock faces

Shores and banks that slope steeply towards the water, or open slope cuts made of unconsolidated materials, are highly important as breeding sites for some bird species that are becoming rare.

02

01 Sand Martins breed in colonies, digging their nest tunnels in sandy or gravelly slopes and banks.

03

02 Like Sand Martins, Bee-eaters (*Merops apiaster*) are colonial tunnel nesters occasionally found breeding at mineral excavation sites.

03 The Common Kingfisher (*Alcedo atthis*) can be encountered in gravel pit lakes with abundant fish, where it fishes from perches in trees or shrubs at the water's edge. It digs a burrow for its nest in steep slopes with a minimum height of 0.5 m.

Creation and preservation of steep faces for colony breeders

01

Sand martins

Sand Martins originally inhabited floodplains where they dug burrows for their nests in steep shores and banks. The creation of artificial breeding walls is a good way of encouraging Sand Martins.

02

01 Steep faces produced during the process of mineral extraction can be suitable for breeding colonies.

02 A Sand Martin (*Riparia riparia*) peering out of its nest burrow.

03 Sand Martins on reedmace. These birds are very sociable.

Bee-eaters

European Bee-eaters, like the Sand Martins mentioned above, can be helped by the creation of steep banks of unconsolidated materials in sand or gravel pits. Their diet consists mainly of big flying insects such as wasps, bumblebees, beetles, and dragonflies. Diverse landscapes with waters, meadows and pastures, where these insects thrive, typically surround Bee-eater breeding sites.

01 Lovers always tease each other.

02 Bee-eaters dig their nest tunnels in sandy soil or loess at heights of not less than 1.5 m.

01

Practical example:

In a gravel pit in Saxony-Anhalt, Germany, Bee-eaters have been breeding since 2009. A total of 13 Bee-eaters were discovered while monitoring Sand Martins. Similarly, in the Ukraine, Bee-eaters were recorded between 2007 and 2009 in the HeidelbergCement plant at Doncement. The preservation of the breeding cliffs has been incorporated into the newly-designed renaturalisation plans.

02

Creation and management of steep faces for Bee-eaters and Sand Martins

Artificial breeding walls can be created in mineral extraction sites by compacting topsoil or sand dumps with heavy machinery, and then cutting them off on the lee side. More expensive solutions are cement walls with sand backfilling, or artificial nest tunnels.

Attention should be paid to the following factors when creating and maintaining steep faces as breeding sites:

- Screes should always be removed in order to keep away predators. The same holds for vegetation on and in front of the breeding walls.
- Woody plants growing in front of the breeding wall can inhibit access and landing for the birds. Shrubs and trees should be removed.
- Ideally, the breeding walls should be higher than 2.5 metres, and face south or southeast. Closeness to water is especially advantageous for Sand Martins.
- Reforestation of the mineral extraction sites, and intensive agriculture in the surrounding areas, will have a negative impact on these species.

In case of conflict with mining plans, when for instance areas that are colonised during the breeding season are scheduled to be excavated, a species management plan can put things right. Following monitoring and documentation of colonised areas during the summer season, the winter can be used for planning. A new steep surface can be created, and the old one be made unattractive by levelling it. This encourages the birds to move to the new breeding wall.

The creation of breeding walls must always be completed by the beginning of April, when the first potential inhabitants (Sand Martins) return. The breeding period of Bee-eaters lasts from the beginning of May through to August.

To maintain Sand Martins and Bee-eater colonies, the breeding wall should be cut off vertically every one to two years with spades or excavator shovels.

01 Steep face with Sand Martin burrows.

02 Bee-eaters like to be close to waters where they may catch large insects such as beetles, dragonflies, or horseflies.

Rock faces

Rock faces in quarries can serve as breeding sites for cliff breeders. However, the design of the quarry, and the nature of the surrounding landscape, are important.

01 A Eurasian Eagle Owl (*Bubo bubo*) snoozing in its day retreat.

02 Like some other rock breeders, the Black Redstart (*Phoenicurus ochruros*) has adapted well to life in human settlements. Its nest sites in quarries are much closer to its original habitat..

03 The Peregrine Falcon (*Falco peregrinus*) is a fast and agile hunter.

04

05

04 Rock faces in quarries offer breeding sites for diverse bird species.

05 The Common Raven (*Corvus corax*) breeds in quarries, especially at higher elevations.

01 Corvids are intelligent and social birds. In many species the young birds stay with their family even after they are fully fledged. Here, a Eurasian Jackdaw (*Corvus monedula*) is begging for food.

02 In rare instances, Little Owls (*Athene noctua*) may colonise rock faces in quarries.

03 If a ruined building like this one is embedded in an agricultural setting…

04 … it may become a breeding place of the Barn Owl (*Tyto alba*).

The Eagle Owl

The Eurasian Eagle Owl is the world's biggest owls. It depends on a diverse cultural landscape for successful nightly hunts. Eagle Owls prefer shallow cavities or ledges in rock faces as nest sites. A little bit of a "roof" is important.

The mating season of Eagle Owls is between mid-January and the end of March. The fledglings are raised between May and July, and between August and September, the young birds disperse. Once they have chosen a breeding site, the adults usually return to it in successive seasons.

01 The breeding success of Eagle Owls needs to be monitored.

02 An Eagle Owl (*Bubo bubo*) breeding on a rock ledge. The pattern of the plumage is excellent camouflage.

Taking care of Eagle Owls

Eagle Owls do not build nests, but deposit their eggs in scrapes in safely inaccessible rocky sites such as rock spurs, ledges and crevices, and platforms left after quarrying. Quarry managers can help increase the availability of such sites, and in this way improve the breeding success of Eagle Owls.

- Create niches with a depth of up to two metres, instead of leaving smooth rock faces.
- During the breeding season, Eagle Owls need access to their breeding sites at all times. When a breeding site is identified, it must be spared from quarrying until the chicks are fully fledged.
- The greater the variety of the rock surfaces and features provided after quarrying, the better Eagle Owls are able to cope with the loss of an old breeding site.
- Breeding niches are most valuable within post-use quarry areas. Such sites should be closed to the public.

Eagle Owls are very susceptible to disturbance at their breeding sites, especially by rock climbers, but also by noise from barbecue parties and so on. Such leisure activities should be banned from areas around known nest sites. However, Eagle Owls may adapt to regular and thus predictable sources of disturbance, such as truck traffic. A quarry which is inaccessible to the public is ideal for an Eagle Owl pair. Breeding success should be monitored by volunteer naturalists, or by experts tasked by the authorities to gather the data needed to improve Eagle Owl management.

03 If an Eagle Owl feels threatened, it performs this aggressive display.

04 The Eagle Owl is an impressive bird, standing up to 75 cm high, with a swing span that can reach 188 cm.

01

02

03

The Peregrine Falcon

The Peregrine Falcon is one of the largest European falcons. It breeds chiefly on rock ledges and spurs. Rock niches also provide typical roosting sites, but the falcons sometimes use abandoned birds' nests. Peregrine Falcons came close to extinction in some European countries in the 1970s. The populations have slowly recovered as a result of intensive conservation actions.

01 Portrait of a young Peregrine Falcon.

02 Peregrine Falcons (*Falco peregrinus*) prey mostly on birds caught in flight, in this case a pigeon.

03 Rock faces with ledges and cavities can provide nesting sites for Peregrine Falcons.

Nest boxes for Peregrine Falcons

Peregrine Falcons can be encountered near their breeding sites all year round. They are swift and agile hunters, striking prey such as feral pigeons in mid-air. They need varied and extensive areas of open terrain over which to hunt.

Like Eagle Owls, Peregrine Falcons can be encouraged to breed by creating rock niches in quarries. Where this is not possible, installing nest boxes is a good alternative.

Nest boxes for Peregrine Falcons consist of a robust box with a wide opening and a large landing board, where the fledglings can practice flying. The box mimics a rock niche with a ledge in front of it. It should be made of durable hardwood or other weather-resistant material. Metal is not recommended. Peregrine Falcons do not use nesting material, so the floor of the box should be lined with coarse sawdust or something similar.

Nest boxes can be installed on smooth rock faces or buildings. The following factors should be considered when selecting the perfect site:

There are projections on the rock face to provide perches for the young falcons. There are no hazards for young birds, such as busy traffic routes or power lines, in the immediate surroundings. The breeding site should be close to open country, and at least 40 metres high. A sheltered lee position exposed to the northeast or southwest is important. The best time for installation is January to February.

Measurements:

- floor area: ca. 70 x 70 cm, at least 50 cm high
- roof area: ca. 90 x 70 cm (with overhang)
- side areas: ca. 50 (55) x 70 cm (3 x)
- iron side with entrance: 30 x 55 cm
- landing board: ca. 70 x 70 cm with
  surrounding rim

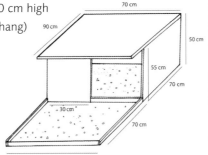

Adapted from: LBV BAYERN (Hrsg.): Nisthilfen. Merkblatt 14, LBV, Hilpoltstein.

Practical examples:

Peregrine Falcons breed regularly in many Heidelberg-Cement quarries. For instance, a pair of Peregrine Falcons has been reproducing successfully for many years within the Leimen quarry near Heidelberg, Germany. To further foster the populations, nest boxes have been installed on many tall plant buildings. This has always been done in close cooperation with local nature conservation organisations.

04

04 Nest box for Peregrine Falcons at the Leimen cement site (Germany).

Shrubby successional areas

When nature is given free rein in post-use mineral extraction sites, tall herbaceous plants (forbs) and woody plants move in by themselves. A mosaic of open spaces and scrub, tall and low vegetation, shaded and sunny areas develops. Such mid-successional "site complexes" are important feeding and breeding habitats for birds and many other animals. Common Stonechats, Common Whitethroats and at warm sites Red-backed Shrikes, may find a home in these areas.

01 The Common Whitethroat (*Sylvia communis*) is a typical bird of shrubby successional vegetation.

02 Common Stonechats (*Saxicola torquatus*) during courtship. The female (on the left) is signalling her readiness for mating.

03 The Red-backed Shrike (*Lanius collurio*) has a hooked beak similar to raptors, with which it catches mice, lizards, and large insects.

04 Dry and warm successional areas are valuable habitats.

Succession

When unconsolidated materials are left alone, so-called pioneer vegetation develops. It is soon displaced by tall forb (herbaceous) vegetation and shrubs. Without human intervention, woodland will develop. This sequence of different plant communities naturally occurring at a site over time is called succession.

Whinchats, and sometimes even rare Bluethroats, may breed in wetlands with reeds and "bulrushes" (*Typha*).

01 The Bluethroat (*Luscinia svecica*) breeds in wet woodlands around standing water.

02 The Whinchat (*Saxicola rubetra*) breeds in open habitats such as rough grasslands with scattered small shrubs.

03 Wet sites with reeds and bushes are habitats of rare bird species.

Grazing for low-maintenance landscape management

When post-use mineral extraction sites are left alone, the vegetation will eventually develop into woodland. This is disadvantageous for species adapted to transitional habitats. In order to preserve mid-successional stages (see side bar p. 87), it is recommended to employ grazing animals such as goats. Goats are very effective at pruning back woody plants, and can reduce shrub encroachment. With good grazing management, mosaics of high and low, dense and sparse vegetation can be created and maintained. The hooves of heavy livestock such as cows and horses create patches of bare ground and puddles which can be colonized by amphibians and aquatic insects. This in turn means increased food availability for birds.

04

05

04 The Tree Pipit (*Anthus trivialis*) is found in late-successional habitats including woodlands with clearings.

05 Post-use quarry with richly structured vegetation.

Fallows and wildlife food plots

Fallows and small-scale extensive arable fields in post-use mineral extraction sites can be valuable habitats, especially when they are connected to copses, hedgerows, forest edges etcetera.

The Grey Partridge

The Grey Partridge once was a common breeding bird of arable fields. It occurred in most agricultural landscapes when these were still interspersed with hedgerows, meadows, and unploughed strips. Land consolidation and the increasing use of pesticides led to an almost complete collapse of the Central European populations. Action to help this species is urgently needed.

01 Release of Grey Partridges in the Schelklingen quarry (Germany).

02 Grey Partridges (*Perdix perdix*) at dusk on a field. Because of intensified use, cropland has become increasingly unsuitable as habitat.

03 Partridges get acquainted with the release aviary.

04 A Grey Partridge just released.

Enhancement of quarries for the Grey Partridge

- The creation of grasslands and of hiding places such as copses is essential.

- In between the copses, species-rich wildlife food plots are important. Plants that are typical of the partridge's diet, such as bistort (*Persicaria bistorta*), should be sown. In most cases, these plots will need to be ploughed every second year.

- These birds like to take sand baths, so open sandy spots are important.

- Throughout the quarry, "wanderbiotopes" should be set up. They are spared from mining activities for variable periods of time, allowing the development of species-rich ruderal vegetation and sparse scrubby areas.

- Finally, permanent water availability is important.

Practical example:

In the Vohenbronnen limestone quarry attached to the Schelklingen cement plant in Germany, new habitats for Grey Partridges were created and the species was re-introduced. The aim was to produce a fine landscape mosaic to meet the habitat requirements of the Grey Partridge. In addition to large meadows, species-rich disturbed ground, hedgerows and groups of trees were established.

In September, 2008, 72 Grey Partridges raised in Germany were released. Most birds were set free right away, but 20 young birds were kept in an aviary and released the following spring.

A regular monitoring programme has been carried out since 2009 to assess the success of the project. A stable population has not yet established itself. The project continues, but casts light on how difficult it can be to re-introduce a bird species once it has gone locally extinct.

04

Nesting aids for other bird species

In all quarries and sand pits, and on private property too, more widespread and less specialised birds can be helped by installing artificial nesting sites. Nest boxes and other nesting aids can be bought or made at home.

01

02

03

01 House Sparrows (*Passer domesticus*) (a female is shown here), are having increasing difficulty finding nest sites in towns, as more and more old buildings are modernised, or fitted with spikes and nets to deter feral pigeons.

04

02 The Eurasian Wryneck (*Jynx torquilla*) is a close relative of woodpeckers. It does not construct its own nest cavity however, and readily accepts nesting boxes.

03 The Great Tit (*Parus major*) is one of the most widespread breeding birds in central Europe.

04 The Wood Nuthatch (*Sitta europaea*) is a cavity breeder. It reduces the entrances of old woodpecker nest holes and nesting boxes by plastering them with clay, so that larger birds can no longer get in. It is the only European bird capable of walking down a tree trunk headfirst.

Recommendations for nesting aids

- Classic nest boxes with an entrance of 3.2 cm are suitable for Great Tits, House Sparrows and Tree Sparrows and Wood Nuthatches. Nest boxes with smaller entrances (2.6 cm) accommodate smaller species such as Blue Tits, Marsh Tits, Coal Tits and Crested Tits. Entrances with a diameter of 5 cm are designed for Common Starlings and Eurasian Wrynecks.

- Black Redstarts, Common Redstarts and Spotted Flycatchers need semi-open nest boxes. As this type of box exposes the nest and the birds are therefore vulnerable predators, it should only be installed in sheltered locations.

- At factory buildings, Northern House Martins can be attracted by installing artificial nests.
  The chances of success are highest when House Martins are already nesting in the neighbourhood.

- It is recommended to install a selection of different nest boxes to support different bird species.

- All nest boxes can be installed on trees or buildings. It is important that predators cannot reach the boxes, so the trunks of trees below the nest box should be free of branches. The entrances should always face away from the prevailing wind and direct sunshine.

- Nest boxes are not only used for breeding, but can also be good roosting sites, especially during cold winter nights. For that reason they should be cleaned at the end of winter, but before the beginning of the new breeding season, ideally at the end of February.

Literature

BAUER, H.-G., E. BEZZEL & W. FIEDLER (2005): Das Kompendium der Vögel Mitteleuropas – Alles über Biologie, Gefährdung und Schutz – Passeriformes – Sperlingsvögel - & Nonpasseriformes – Nichtsperlingsvögel – AULA-Verlag (Wiebelsheim), 622 resp. 808 pages.

BERMANN, H.-H. (1987): Die Biologie des Vogels – Eine exemplarische Einführung in Bau, Funktion und Lebensweise – AULA-Verlag (Wiebelsheim), 356 pages.

BEZZEL, E. (1982): Vögel der Kulturlandschaft – Ulmer-Verlag (Stuttgart), 350 pages.

BUNDESVERBAND BAUSTOFFE – STEINE UND ERDEN E. V., NATUR-SCHUTZBUND DEUTSCHLAND (NABU) (2010): Betreiber von Steinbrüchen und Gruben sichern den Lebensraum von Uhus, Flyer.

GILCHER, S. & D. BRUNS (1999): Renaturierung von Abbaustätten – Ulmer-Verlag (Stuttgart), 355 pages.

HÖLZINGER, J. (1987-1999): Die Vögel Baden-Württembergs – Gefährdung und Schutz – Teil 1 – Singvögel 1 & 2 – Band 3.1 & 3.2. – Ulmer-Verlag (Stuttgart), 719, 861 resp. 939 pages.

HÖLZINGER, J. & M. BOSCHERT (2001): Die Vögel Baden-Württembergs. – Nicht-Singvögel 2 – Band 2.2 – Ulmer-Verlag (Stuttgart), 880 pages.

HÖLZINGER, J. & U. MAHLER (2001): Die Vögel Baden-Württembergs – Nicht-Singvögel 3 – Band 2.3 – Ulmer-Verlag (Stuttgart), 547 pages.

INULA (2011): Dragonflies in quarries and gravel pits. – Biodiversity in mineral extraction sites, vol. 1. Editor: M. Rademacher, Global Management Biodiversity and Natural resources, HeidelbergCement, 98 pages.

INULA (2012): Orchids in quarries and gravel pits. – Biodiversity in mineral extraction sites, vol. 2. Editor: M. Rademacher, Global Management Biodiversity and Natural resources, HeidelbergCement, 98 pages.

MAYR, G., B. POHL & D. S. PETERS (2005): A well-preserved Archaeopteryx specimen with theropod features – Science 310 (5753): 1483 – 1486.

PEPPERBERG, I. M. (2009): Alex und ich. Die einzigartige Freundschaft zwischen einer Harvard-Forscherin und dem schlausten Vogel der Welt – mvg Verlag (München), 208 pages.

STEPHAN, B. (1987): Urvögel. 3. Auflage – Ziemsen-Verlag (Wittenberg), 216 pages.

SVENSSON, L., K. MULLARNEY & D. ZETTERSTRÖM (2011): Der Kosmos-Vogelführer. Alle Arten Europas, Nordafrikas und Vorderasiens, 2nd edition – Franckh-Kosmos Verlag (Stuttgart), 448 pages.

RUTZ, C., L. A. BLUFF, N. REED, J. TROSCIANKO, J. NEWTON, R. INGER, A. KACELNIK & S. BEARHOP (2010): The ecological significance of tool use in New Caledonian crows – Science 329 (5998): 1523 – 1526.

WEMBER, V. (2007): Die Namen der Vögel Europas – AULA-Verlag (Wiebelsheim), 250 pages.

XU, X., H. YOU, K. DU & F. HAN (2011): An Archaeopteryx-like theropod from China and the origin of the Avialae – Nature 475: 465 – 470.

Internet sources:

http://de/wikipedia.org, http://en.wikipedia.org

http://www.birdlife.org/

Magnetic sense and UV-detection:
http://www.scinexx.de/wissen-aktuell-5171-2006-08-11.html
http://www.muk.uni-frankfurt.de/38894307/122

Winner of the Quarry Life Awards 2012:
http://www.quarrylifeaward.com/project/restoration-quarry-silt-lagoons-wading-birds

Imprint

ISBN 978-3-9815050-4-7

Editor
Dr. Michael Rademacher, Global Manager Biodiversity & Natural Resources, HeidelbergCement

Production
INULA – Institut für Naturschutz und Landschaftsanalyse, Freiburg i. Br., www.inula.de

Conception
Dipl.-Biol. Dr. Holger Hunger & Dipl.-Biol. Franz-Josef Schiel (INULA), Dipl.-Biol. Dr. Michael Rademacher (HeidelbergCement)

Layout, setting, design
Werbeagentur ServiceDesign, www.servicedesign.eu

Text
Dipl.-Biologen Kerstin Geigenbauer, Dr. Holger Hunger & Franz-Josef Schiel (INULA)

Translation
Dr. Holger Hunger & Nick Langley

Scientific language advisor
Prof. Dr. Burton V. Barnes, Ann Arbor, Michigan (USA)

Drawings
Dipl.-Biol. Kerstin Geigenbauer

Photographs
Yves Adams – Vilda (p. 21: 05), Arne Ader (p. 68: 03), Boris Belchev – www.alcedowildlife.com (p. 67: 04, 05; 79: 05), Klaus Bittner (p. 82: 02; 88: 02), Andrius Ceponis (p. 25: 02; 53: 04; 62: 01), Luis Ferreira (p. 83: 04), Hans Glader (p. 40: 01; 54: 02; 61: 03), Tina Gölzer (p. 90: 01, 03), Erich Greiner (p. 31: 02; 37: 02), Gareth Henwood (p. 63: 03), Lubomir Hlasek (p. 29: 02; 32: 01; 78: 01; 80: 01; 86: 01), Luc Hoogenstein (p. 8; 13: 03; 48: 02; 49: 03, 04), INULA (p. 38; 40: 02; 41: 03; 42: 01; 43: 03; 44: 01, 02; 48: 01; 50: 01; 52: 01; 53: 05; 55: 03; 58: 01; 66: 02; 67: 03; 69: 01; 70: 01; 79: 04; 81: 03; 84: 03; 87: 04; 88: 03; 89: 05), Mati Kose (p. 29: 03; 92: 02), Bruno Maia (p. 10: 02; 11: 4; 20: 1; 26: 1; 51: 3; 56: 2; 71: 3; 81: 4; 84: 2; 86: 2), Ralph Martin (p. 43: 04; 46-47 ; 56: 01; 66: 01; 68: 02; 78: 02), Nicky Petkov (p. 10: 01; 23: 03; 36: 01; 70: 02), Alen Ploj (p. 80: 02), Mathias Putze – www.green-lens.de (p. 22: 01; 45: 03; 54: 01; 59: 03; 62: 02; 73: 03), Stefan Pfützke – www.green-lens.de (p. 20: 02; p. 21: 03; 52: 02; 57: 03), Michael Rademacher (p. 64: 01, 02; 72: 01; 75: 02; 77: 01, 02), Jochen Roeder (p. 18: 01; 63: 04; 82: 01, 03; 84: 01; 85: 04; 91: 04), Rosl Rössner (p. 12: 01; 16: 01; 19: 02, 03; 23: 02; 26: 02; 31: 03; 30: 01; 90: 02), Lars Soerink – Vilda (p. 32: 02; 34: 01, 02; 42: 02; 51: 02; 52: 03; 60: 01; 69: 04; 87: 03; 88: 01), Svetoslav Sparov – www.natureimages.eu (p. 11: 03; 27: 03; 35: 04; 60: 02; 74: 01), David Veer (p. 12: 02; 14: 01, 03; 21: 04; 24: 01; 33: 03; 92: 01, 03; 93: 04), Milan Vogrin (p. 15: 02; 51: 04), Ralf Weise (p. 29: 01; 35: 03; 58: 02; 72: 02; 78: 03; 89: 04). Cover picture: European Bee-eater (Photo by Rosl Rössner).

Recommended form of citation
INULA (2013): Birds in quarries and gravel pits. – Biodiversity in mineral extraction sites, volume 3.
Editor: M. Rademacher, Global Management Biodiversity and Natural Resources, HeidelbergCement, 98 pp.

HEIDELBERGCEMENT